Play Easy Recorder

Published by:
Chester Music Limited
8/9 Frith Street, London W1D 3JB, England.

Exclusive distributors:
Music Sales Limited
Distribution Centre, Newmarket Road,
Bury St. Edmunds, Suffolk IP33 3YB.

Music Sales Pty Limited
120 Rothschild Avenue, Rosebery,
NSW 2018, Australia.

Order No. CH66825
ISBN 1-84449-065-3
This book © Copyright 2003 by Chester Music.

Compiled by Heather Ramage.
All arrangements by Jerry Lanning
unless stated otherwise.
Music engraved by Jerry Lanning.
Cover designed by Ian Butterworth Design.
Printed in UK by Caligraving.

www.musicsales.com

Chester Music Limited
London / New York / Paris / Sydney /
Copenhagen / Berlin / Madrid / Tokyo

Volume 2

American Pie

Words & Music by Don McLean

Matchmaker

(from "Fiddler On The Roof")
Words by Sheldon Harnick. Music by Jerry Bock

Bali Ha'i

(from "South Pacific")
Words by Oscar Hammerstein II. Music by Richard Rodgers

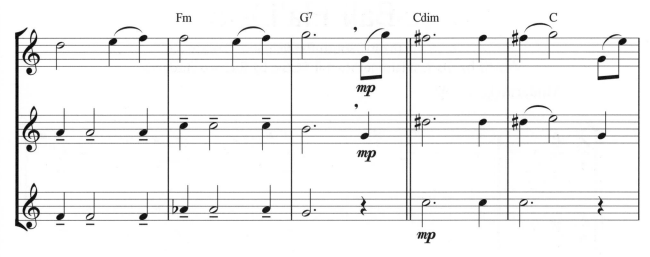

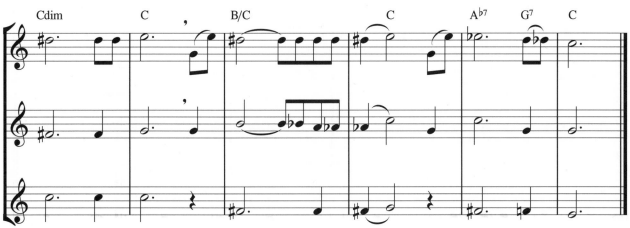

Bali Ha'i may call you
Any night, any day.
In your heart you'll hear it call you:
"Come away, come away."

Bali Ha'i will whisper
On the wind of the sea:
"Here am I, your special island!
Come to me, come to me!"

Your own special hopes,
Your own special dreams
Bloom on the hillside
And shine in the streams.

If you try, you'll find me
Where the sky meets the sea.
"Here am I, your special island!
Come to me, come to me!"

Close Every Door

(from "Joseph And The Amazing Technicolor Dreamcoat")
Words by Tim Rice. Music by Andrew Lloyd Webber

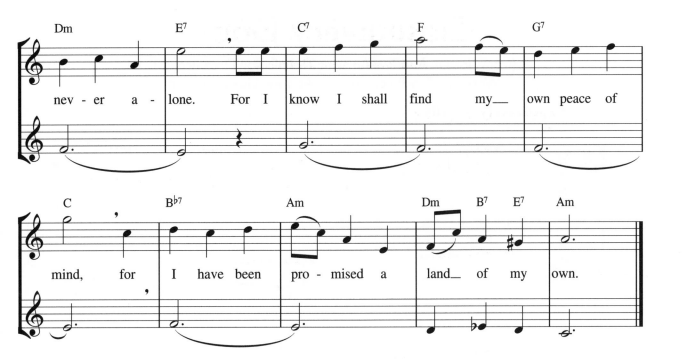

Dm | E⁷ | C⁷ | F | G⁷

nev-er a-lone. For I know I shall find my— own peace of

C | B♭⁷ | Am | Dm | B⁷ E⁷ | Am

mind, for I have been pro-mised a land— of my own.

Do Your Ears Hang Low?

Traditional

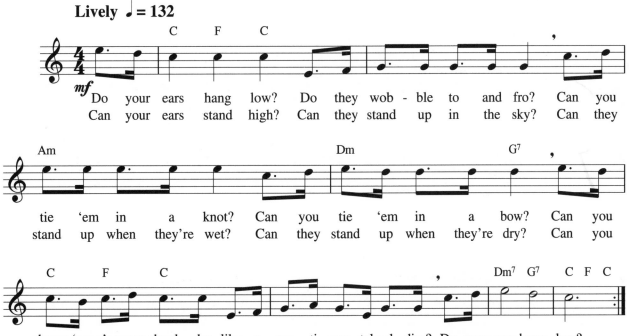

Lively ♩ = 132

mf

Do your ears hang low? Do they wob-ble to and fro? Can you
Can your ears stand high? Can they stand up in the sky? Can they

tie 'em in a knot? Can you tie 'em in a bow? Can you
stand up when they're wet? Can they stand up when they're dry? Can you

throw 'em o'er your shoul-der like a con-ti-nen-tal sol-dier? Do your ears hang low?
wave them to your neigh-bour with the min-i-mum of la-bour? Can your ears stand high?

7

Londonderry Air

Traditional Irish Folk Melody

Edelweiss

(from "The Sound Of Music")
Words by Oscar Hammerstein II
Music by Richard Rodgers

Alla Danza

(from "Water Music")
By George Frideric Handel
Arranged by Emma Coulthard

11

It's Raining, It's Pouring

Traditional

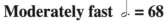

Moderately fast ♩. = 68

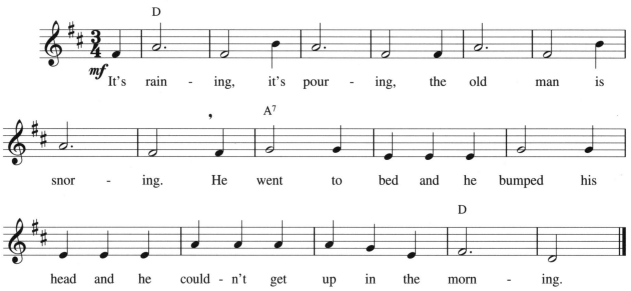

It's rain - ing, it's pour - ing, the old man is snor - ing. He went to bed and he bumped his head and he could - n't get up in the morn - ing.

I'm Popeye The Sailor Man

Words & Music by Sammy Lerner

Lively ♩. = 88

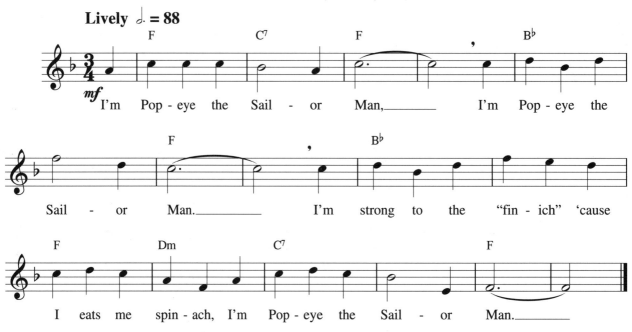

I'm Pop - eye the Sail - or Man,_____ I'm Pop - eye the Sail - or Man._____ I'm strong to the "fin - ich" 'cause I eats me spin - ach, I'm Pop - eye the Sail - or Man._____

Lullaby

By Johannes Brahms

No Matter What

Music by Andrew Lloyd Webber
Words by Jim Steinman

can't de - ny___ what I be - lieve, I can't be what I'm not.

I know our love's for ev - er, I know no mat - ter what.___ I

can't de - ny___ what I be - lieve, I can't be what I'm not.

I know our love's for ev - er, I know no mat - ter what.___

Ode To Joy

(from "Symphony No.9")
By Ludwig van Beethoven

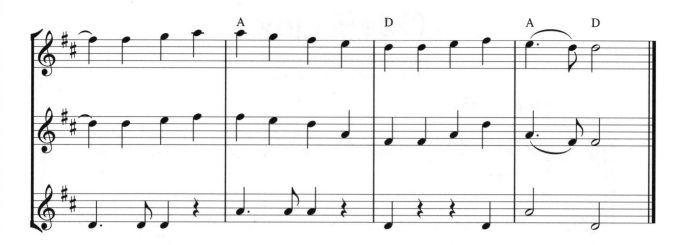

Jean de Florette (Theme)

By Jean-Claude Petit

Li'l Liza Jane

Traditional American Folk Ballad

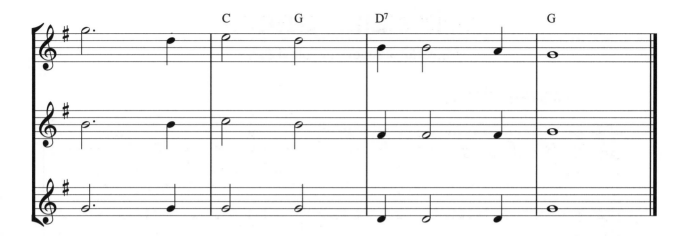

I know a gal that I adore,
Li'l Liza Jane.
'Way down south in Baltimore,
Li'l Liza Jane.
Oh, Eliza, Li'l Liza Jane!
Oh, Eliza, Li'l Liza Jane!

On Top Of Old Smoky

Traditional Kentucky Mountain Folksong

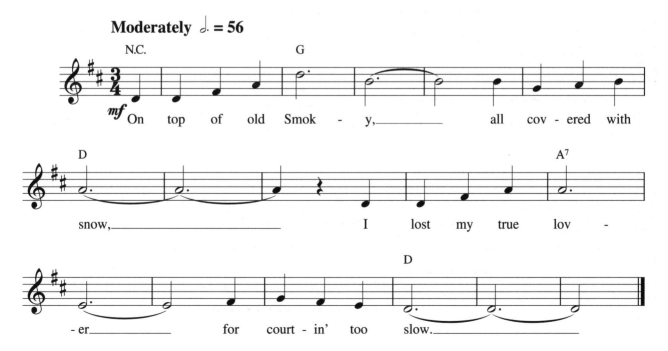

Moderately ♩. = 56

On top of old Smok - y,_____ all cov - ered with snow,_____ I lost my true lov - er_____ for court - in' too slow._____

Somethin' Stupid

Words & Music by C. Carson Parks

And then I go and spoil it all by

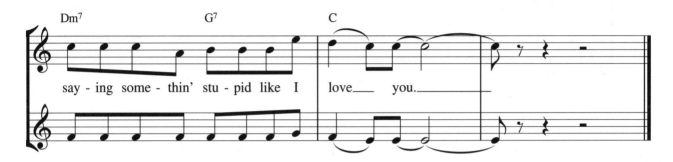

say - ing some - thin' stu - pid like I love___ you.___

Jolly Old St. Nicholas

Traditional

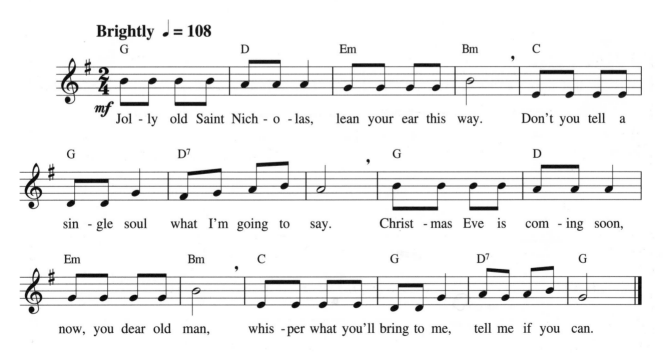

Brightly ♩ = 108

Jol - ly old Saint Nich - o - las, lean your ear this way. Don't you tell a

sin - gle soul what I'm going to say. Christ - mas Eve is com - ing soon,

now, you dear old man, whis - per what you'll bring to me, tell me if you can.

Silent Night

Words by Joseph Mohr
Music by Franz Grüber

The First Noel

Traditional

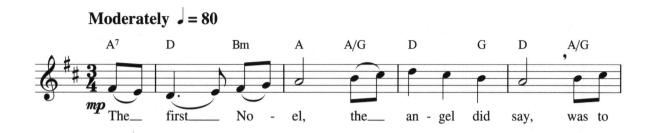

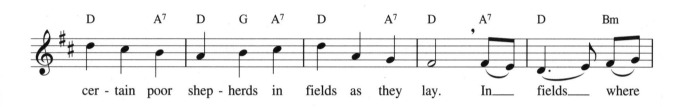

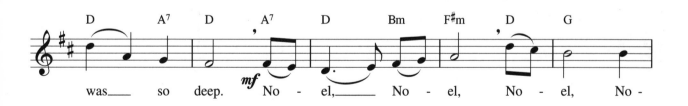

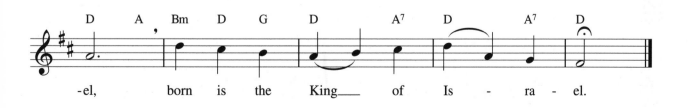

She's Leaving Home

Words & Music by John Lennon & Paul McCartney

To A Wild Rose

By Edward MacDowell

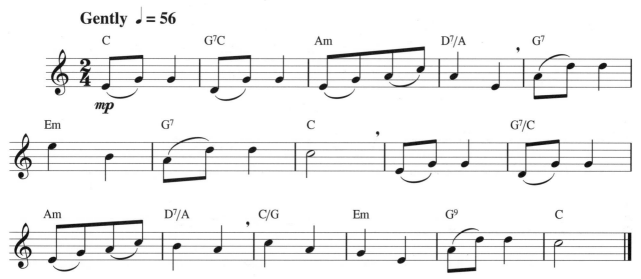

London Bridge

Traditional

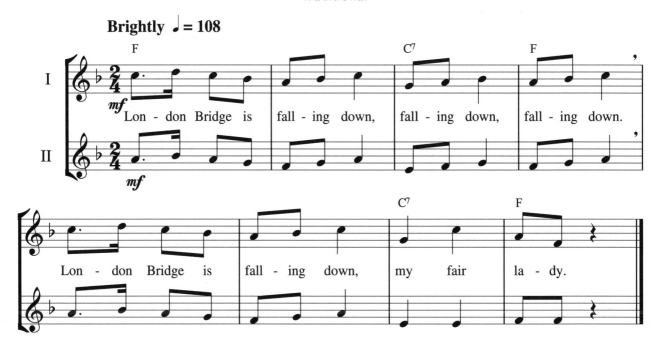

Supercalifragilisticexpialidocious

Words & Music by Richard M. Sherman & Robert B. Sherman

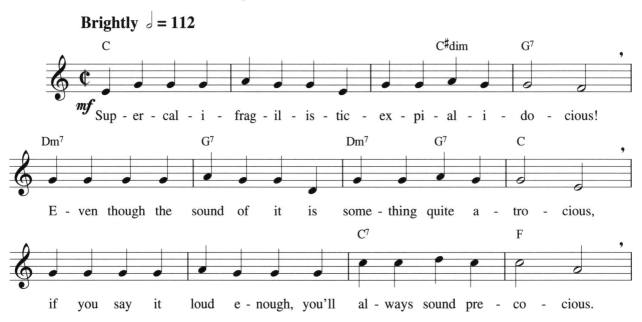

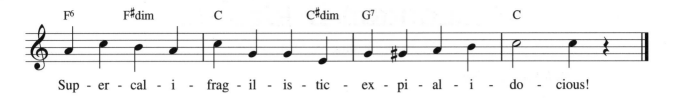

Sup - er - cal - i - frag - il - is - tic - ex - pi - al - i - do - cious!

'Surprise' Symphony

(Slow Movement)
By Franz Joseph Haydn

Pick A Pocket Or Two

Words & Music by Lionel Bart

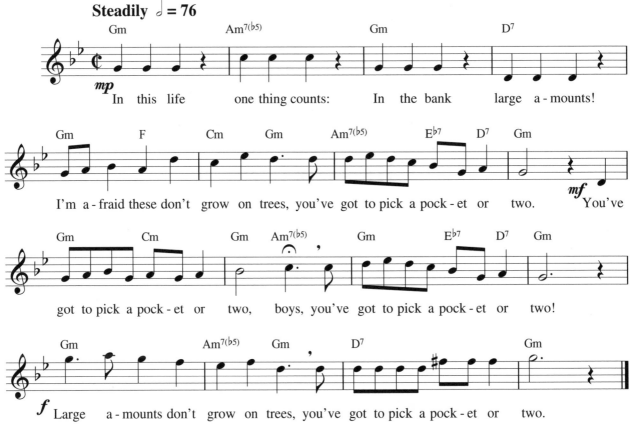

Steadily ♩ = 76

In this life one thing counts: In the bank large a-mounts! I'm a-fraid these don't grow on trees, you've got to pick a pock-et or two. You've got to pick a pock-et or two, boys, you've got to pick a pock-et or two! Large a-mounts don't grow on trees, you've got to pick a pock-et or two.

It's A Small World

Words & Music by Richard M. Sherman & Robert B. Sherman

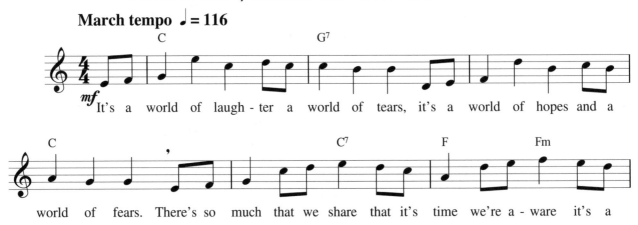

March tempo ♩ = 116

It's a world of laugh-ter a world of tears, it's a world of hopes and a world of fears. There's so much that we share that it's time we're a-ware it's a

small world af - ter all. It's a small world af - ter all, it's a small world

af - ter all, it's a small world af - ter all, it's a small, small world.

Oh! Susanna

Words & Music by Stephen C. Foster

I come from Al - a - bam - a with a ban - jo on my knee. I'm

goin' to Loui - si - an - a my Su - san - na for to see. It rained all night the

day I left, the weath - er it was dry. The sun so hot I froze to death, Su -

- san - na don't you cry. Oh! Su - san - na, oh don't you cry for

me, for I come from Al - a - bam - a with a ban - jo on my knee.

The Big Rock Candy Mountain

Traditional American Hobo Song

blue - bird sings, in the Big Rock Can - dy Moun - tain.

La Donna è Mobile

(from "Rigoletto")
By Giuseppe Verdi

If you enjoyed using this book, why not try *these*...

Play Easy Recorder: Volume 1

A great collection of familiar tunes arranged for easy recorder. Contains solo, duet and trio arrangements with lyrics and guitar chords.

Includes...
Amazing Grace
All Love Can Be *from* **'A Beautiful Mind'**
Can-Can
EastEnders Theme
Moon River
Pelagia's Song *from* **'Captain Corelli's Mandolin'**
Whole Again
...and many more!

Play Easy Recorder: Christmas

All the best known carols and songs arranged for easy recorder. Contains solo, duet and trio arrangements with lyrics and guitar chords. Perfect repertoire for Christmas concerts or just for fun!

Includes...
Angels From The Realms Of Glory
Coventry Carol
Deck The Halls
I Saw Three Ships
O Christmas Tree
O Little Town Of Bethlehem
We Three Kings
Frosty The Snowman
Mistletoe and Wine
Winter Wonderland
...and many more!

For more information on these and the thousands of other titles available from Chester Music and Music Sales, please contact:

Music Sales Limited
Newmarket Road, Bury St Edmunds, Suffolk, IP33 3YB.
Tel: 01284 702600. Fax: 01284 768301.
www.musicsales.com